Burning Bird

A play

John Donnelly

CW00553085

SERVING THEATRE

SINCE 1830

Samuel French — London
www.samuelfrench-london.co.uk

BURNING BIRD

Commissioned and first presented by Synergy Theatre Project at the Unicorn Theatre on 14 November 2012 following a tour to schools across London.

Daisy	Simone James
Tyrone	Valentine Olukoga
Bev/Yvonne	Debbie Samuel
Morell/Roy	Michael Smith
Mr Akhtar/Mr Johnson	Anil Kumar
Miss Lyons/Jacqui	Catherine Nix-Collins

All other parts played by the company

Director	Esther Baker
Designer	Katy McPhee
Lighting Designer	Shane Burke
Costume Designer	Sophia Simensky
Sound Designer	Sarah Weltman
Video Designer	Chris Beston
Casting Director	Nadine Rennie CDG
Company Stage Manager	Rupert Carlile
Assistant Stage Managers	Ronnie Actil
	and David Frederick

Artistic Director	**Esther Baker**
General Manager	**Jennie McClure**
New Writing Manager	**Neil Grutchfield**
Education Manager	**Kirstin Shirling**

www.synergytheatreproject.co.uk

The UK's leading theatre for audiences aged 2-21
www.unicorntheatre.com

Supported by:
The Monument Trust
The City Bridge Trust

LOTTERY FUNDED

COPYRIGHT INFORMATION

(See also page ii)

This play is fully protected under the Copyright Laws of the British Commonwealth of Nations, the United States of America and all countries of the Berne and Universal Copyright Conventions.

All rights including Stage, Motion Picture, Radio, Television, Public Reading, and Translation into Foreign Languages, are strictly reserved.

No part of this publication may lawfully be reproduced in ANY form or by any means — photocopying, typescript, recording (including video-recording), manuscript, electronic, mechanical, or otherwise — or be transmitted or stored in a retrieval system, without prior permission.

Licences for amateur performances are issued subject to the understanding that it shall be made clear in all advertising matter that the audience will witness an amateur performance; that the names of the authors of the plays shall be included on all programmes; and that the integrity of the authors' work will be preserved.

The Royalty Fee is subject to contract and subject to variation at the sole discretion of Samuel French Ltd.

In Theatres or Halls seating Four Hundred or more the fee will be subject to negotiation.

In Territories Overseas the fee quoted above may not apply. A fee will be quoted on application to our local authorized agent, or if there is no such agent, on application to Samuel French Ltd, London.

Video-Recording Of Amateur Productions

Please note that the copyright laws governing video-recording are extremely complex and that it should not be assumed that any play may be video-recorded for *whatever purpose* without first obtaining the permission of the appropriate agents. The fact that a play is published by Samuel French Ltd does not indicate that video rights are available or that Samuel French Ltd controls such rights.

Children and Performance Legislation

For any productions utilizing children, producers will need to be aware of the appropriate child safeguarding and children in performance legislation in place. For details of the requirements you should contact your local County Council child performance advisor.

CHARACTERS

Daisy
Tyrone
Bev
Morell
Mr Akhtar
Teresa
Miss Lyons
Mr Johnson
Inspector
Jacqui
Yvonne
Landlord Mick
Roy
Girl
Girl 2
Writer
Guy

The action of the play takes place in various locations around South London

Time—the present

Production Notes

The company should create the world of the play.

Scenes should be announced by the company.

Entrances, exits, pauses and stage directions should be inferred from the text. Occasionally, for clarity, these are provided.

A hyphen (–) denotes a line taken by a member or members of the company.

A slash (/) denotes the point at which the following cue begins.

The company should acknowledge the audience throughout and often will address them directly.

BURNING BIRD

— Whose story is this?
— 'Cause someone's always in charge.
— And you got to ask yourself why they're telling the story.
— This is a story about Daisy.
— And who is Daisy?

Daisy Leave me alone!

— Daisy is in bed.

Daisy I'm sleeping.

— As you can see, she's not really sleeping.

Daisy Not any more I'm not.

— This is her friend Tyrone.

Tyrone Hello, I'm Tyrone.

— Just said that.

Tyrone Sorry / I thought you wanted me.

— And her mum, B —— I'm talking!

Tyrone Sorry.

— And Bev.

Bev Oh stop.

— Bev is Daisy's Mum.

Bev I get embarrassed.

— And Morell.

Morell All right.

— Some of these people you will like more than others.

Morell How you doing?

— Will you stop it, man?

Morell I'm just talking.

— Always doing this.

Morell Making conversation with the nice people.
Akhtar I am Mr Akhtar.

— He not got a first name?
— We don't know his first name.

Akhtar Ravi.

— But we don't need to know that.

Morell Everyone just calls him Mr Akhtar.
Akhtar My wife calls me Ravi.

— We don't meet your wife.

Akhtar She's in the hospital, gall bladder, I'm worried / it's ——

— There are other people in the story.
— Played by us.
— There's reporters.
— Police.
— Bus conductors.
— Rioters.
— They ain't rioters.
— People causing a civil disturbance.
— Kicking in JD Sports more like.
— Nicking some trainers more like.
— We will bring all these people into this, this — what is this?
— This is a pub.
— This is a retail shopping outlet.
— These are the school gates.

— This is a classroom.
— The junction of a road.
— Ting ting.
— This is Mr Akhtar's shop.
— Ting ting.

Akhtar One bloody Asian in the play, they give me a corner shop.

— Ting ting.

Akhtar Will you stop doing that?

— Every time someone comes in or out.
— Ting ting.
— It makes that noise.
— Ting ting.

Akhtar Stop doing that!

— This is Morell's car.
— Vroom Vroom!
— What is that?

Morell That's my ride.

— That ain't no ride, just a person making a broom broom noise.

Morell Trust me, it's a ride.

— What? You run out of budget?
— This is all these places and more.

Daisy Uh, pervert, this is my bedroom, how about some privacy?

— All right all right.
— This is a play in ten scenes.
— Ten!
— Short scenes.
— Short-ish.
— It starts with Daisy at home and it will end with Daisy at home.
— There will be thrills and spills.
— Cars and bars.
— People on the streets.

— But by the time Daisy gets home ...
— Everything will have changed.

Scene 1

— The first scene!
— Which begins with —

Daisy Bart Simpson is looking at me. He has a skateboard tucked under his arm and in the middle of the skateboard there is a digital readout that says —

— Seven-thirteen a.m.
— That's thirteen minutes past seven in the morning for anyone old, like over thirty.

Daisy Light creeps round the curtains, bathes my face in warmth. Last few seconds before ——

— Beep Beep Beep Beep.

Daisy Ain't normally good in the morning, ain't normally good full stop but today it's different, today I'm ——
Bev What's that racket?
Daisy Jump the stairs, two, three at a time, hear my mum call ——
Bev Like a herd of elephants in my house.
Daisy Front door. Check the mat —

— Nothing.

Daisy I look on the side next to the bills and leaflets for some scratchy new takeaway with food poisoning on the menu.

— Nothing.

Daisy Nothing.
Bev It's probably nothing.
Daisy Mum pokes her head round the kitchen door, unlit fag in her mouth.
Thought you'd quit?
Bev I have, just need something there, you know, and I don't chew gum.
Daisy How come you need a lighter if you don't smoke?

Bev Come get your toast.

Daisy Don't want toast.

Bev Butter and Sunpat.

Daisy I don't want butter and Sunpat.

Bev Come get your tea.

Daisy Don't want no tea.

Bev Made it milky, two sugars, how you like it. Made it in a pot.

Daisy My mum she makes the best tea.

Bev It's true my tea is good, milk first then the water.

Daisy It ain't here.

Bev First post ain't never come at this time, darlin'. Don't worry, it'll come. I'm sure.

Reporter A black male was shot by police yesterday afternoon.

Daisy Some craziness north of the river.

Reporter The thirty-one year old, believed to be jobless, was known to the police.

Bev So young.

Daisy Thirty-one is old!

Bev Ain't that much younger than me.

Daisy Exactly.

Bev I don't care what he done, you can't go round shooting people.

Reporter Tensions running high in the capital, police and spokespersons from the community are appealing for calm.

Bev Spokespersons of the community?

Daisy I stare at the letterbox.

Bev Only time these persons start speaking is when there's TV cameras pointing.

Bev notices Daisy is staring at the letterbox

Bev Darling. You OK?

Daisy This is the thing with my mum, right, she always got to poke her nose in. Why can't she leave me be? It's 'cause she's lonely. I'll tell you what she needs, right, she needs a man. I know why she got that hungry look about her, I know how come she all itchy and scratchy in the mornings ——

Bev My little girl may act all tough but don't be impressed. I worry about the company she keeps, where she goes. I had her too young. And by the way, that is a lie, I do not need a man, making me sound like some alley cat.

Daisy She got that look.

Bev All right, maybe it has been a while, but I am not some sex maniac, all right.

Daisy Like she about to say something dumb.
Bev Maybe this'll cheer you up.
Daisy What is it?
Bev It's from me. Open it.
Bev For your interviews.
Daisy What interviews?
Bev University?
Daisy Mum, I'm Year Ten!
Bev I want you to make something of yourself.
Daisy We can't afford university.
Bev You can get a loan.
Daisy You gave me a folder on my birthday?
Bev You gotta do something, can't just sit on your backside all your life. It's faux leather.
Daisy Oh faux leather!
Bev Would have got real leather but I know you don't like that. See you're wearing the earrings Dad gave you last year.
Daisy You got a problem with that?
Bev I'm just saying, don't get disappointed / if he doesn't ——
Daisy Don't say it! Don't!
Bev I'm just saying, don't get your hopes up.
Daisy I'm gonna be late.
Bev Daisy ——
Daisy Oh you want me to be late for school now?
Bev Darling, be careful out there, news says there might be trouble later. Come straight home.
Daisy I ain't no child.
Bev You don't know what's good for you.
Daisy You can talk, you're the one smokes cigarettes.
Bev That's totally different.
Daisy Is it now?
Bev Make sure you keep your phone on!

SCENE 2

— Ting Ting!

— **Scene Two.**
— **In which Daisy tries to buy crisps and a drink but is thwarted due to insufficient funds.**

Akhtar Wait!

Daisy What?

Akhtar You see the sign?

Daisy Come on, man.

Akhtar What does it say?

Daisy I ain't wearing my hoodie up.

Akhtar The other sign.

Daisy One child at a time.

Akhtar When she is gone, you can come in.

Daisy That's Teresa, always giving me the up and down eyes like she better than me. Hurry up, man, I'm waiting.

Teresa I'm choosing.

Daisy Well choose faster.

Akhtar No trouble please.

Daisy Come on, Mr Akhtar, I just want a drink and some crisps.

Akhtar When your friend has gone.

Daisy She ain't my friend. Look at her, taking her time on purpose, trying to make me late. (*She kisses her teeth*)

Akhtar Every time kids come in, they cause trouble, always stealing, always taking things. That's why I have the sign.

Daisy One in, one out, like we're criminals or something, like we second class, got to stand here in the doorway like a lemon.

Akhtar I have kids of my own, grown up now. I know it's hard, they have nowhere to go, but I'm not a charity. One pound twenty-eight, I don't care how hard your home life is. You're not going to convince me that stealing a can of ginger beer is a result of a deprived childhood.

Daisy (*to Teresa*) What's that look about? You got something to say to me, you best say it.

— Ting ting.

Akhtar These bloody accounts never add up, probably 'cause of all the chocolate bars that just walk out of here of their own accord.
Please take your hood down.

Daisy It's an item of clothing, not a lethal weapon.

Akhtar No helmets, no hoods, that's the rules, you don't like them, go somewhere else.

Daisy Treat me like I'm worthless.

Daisy obliges with her hood

Akhtar Thank you. Are you going to buy anything?

Daisy Crisps and a coke.

Akhtar Do you not have breakfast?

Daisy Who are you, Jamie Oliver?

Akhtar One pound nine pence. That's one pound seven. Two pence more.

Daisy It's all I got.

Akhtar Two pence more.

Daisy I'll owe it you.

Akhtar Credit's what got this country in so much damn trouble, you want something you pay for it.

Daisy I come here all the time.

Akhtar You want crisps and a drink, those aren't in your price range, these ones are.

Daisy Don't want Chipsticks, want Monster Munch.

Akhtar Well I want a house in the country and Arsenal to win the league but sometimes life isn't fair, come on, two more pence or the cheaper ones.

Daisy This shop is only here because we come in here, look how you treat us.

Akhtar She has a point. Kids buy all their sweets from here. Between them and the strange men who come in for the naughty magazines on the top shelf, that's my customer base. Confectionery, naked ladies, and tobacco, this is what makes this country great.

Daisy Maybe this is the day I snap, tell him what I think of his signs and his looks and his attitude.

Akhtar We all have to make a living. My wife is not well, she's in hospital. Her gall bladder, nothing serious, but — thank God for the bloody NHS. They say she needs an operation. Things aren't going so well with the shop. I don't sleep.

Daisy Half a mind to tip his display over, take my drink, throw it straight through his window, that'll show him.

Akhtar Maybe I'm being too hard on the girl, she's just a child. Maybe I'll let her off, just this once, maybe I'll ——

Daisy Forget about it.

— Ting ting!

Akhtar No pleasing some people.

SCENE 3

— **Scene Three.**

— **In which Daisy makes a paper crane and gets in trouble with one of her teachers.**

Tyrone You see it on the news? Daisy, you see it on the news, Daisy?

Daisy Tyrone waits at the gates, like he does everyday. Sits next to me in Art and Science. I like him. He lets me copy his homework. See what? As if I don't know. As if everyone ain't talking about it.

— Heard he was a gangster.
— Heard it was revenge.
— Heard he wasn't carrying a gun.
— Heard he was a terrorist!

Tyrone That guy who got shot, that was bad, man.

— They don't shoot someone for no reason.
— No smoke without fire.
— He was just some guy minding his own business.

Daisy Everyone's an expert.

Tyrone Gonna be people out in force.

Daisy Says who?

Tyrone Chatrooms, BBM is going off! Word is they might let us out school early.

Daisy Why they do that?

Tyrone Temperature's rising, you get me? Feel the steam coming off the sidewalks.

Daisy He does this, Tyrone, he gets excited, starts talking like an American.

Tyrone There's gonna be a curfew, I'm telling you.

Daisy Ain't gonna be no curfew, this ain't no police state like, like —

— Syria.
— Egypt.
— Cyprus.

Daisy Thank you. You need to stop watching the news. It gives you ideas. Ain't no terrorists in South London! North London, mind you, that's a whole different story, but South London, just kids with Blackberrys and attitude.

Tyrone What you reckon, Daisy, it goes off will you go and have a look?

Daisy Wants so hard to be one of them bad boys, T. But he's just a puppy.

— Vroom vrooom! Vroom vroom!

— Nice ride, man.
— Nice rims.
— That car is set.
— Whose car is that?

Daisy Morell's car.
Tyrone André Morell.
Daisy But everyone calls him Morell.
Tyrone He's one of them cats don't have a first name.
Daisy Round here, everyone knows who Morell is.

— Bet even his mum calls him Morell.

Daisy He don't live with his mum.

— Who's he live with?

Tyrone His uncle.
Daisy You like that car, Tyrone?
Tyrone 'S'all right.
Morell Hey Daisy, Daisy Duke.
Daisy This what he calls me, Daisy Duke. Like in that film — Dukes of Hazzard.
Morell Wanna ride?
Tyrone She got school.
Morell Was I talking to you?
Daisy Where you going?
Morell Wherever you want.

— Vroom Vroom!

Daisy Guns the engine like a bodybuilder flexing a bicep. Everyone staring. All these people, kids, teachers, I see the way they look at me.
Tyrone Ain't even his ride, it's his uncle's, he owns a second hand car place on the High Street.
Daisy Like Teresa, sket from the shop, looking all the way down her pointy nose at me. Don't matter why no one looks at you just so long as they do. Reasons is small print.

— Vroom vroom!

Daisy Shall I get in? Shall I not? Go left, go right. Decisions, decisions.
Tyrone Come on, Daisy, let's go.

Morell You want to hang out with a real man. Not little boy lost there.

Miss Lyons Bell's gone, Daisy, time for class.

Morell Hello, Miss Lyons. How you doing, Miss Lyons? Looking fine, Miss Lyons.

Tyrone That's Miss Lyons, she is quite pretty.

Morell You can come too if you like, Miss Lyons. Always welcome to come with me, Miss Lyons.

Miss Lyons Remember your first day here, Andre? Year Seven? 'Cause I do. You came crying to me 'cause someone made a peanut of your tie.

Morell I ain't no kid no more.

Miss Lyons Oh, you're a man now?

Morell That's right, miss, I am. And you best remember that. Laters.

— Vrooom! Vrooom!

Daisy I know what Morell wants. I might be stupid, but I ain't desperate.

Miss Lyons So whose company do we have the pleasure of today? Good Daisy or Bad Daisy?

Daisy Every day she asks me this, every day I say, "Good Daisy, miss." Always Good Daisy. Watch her walk towards C Block, offering a hand here, a kind word there. Miss Lyons tells me I can do stuff, be someone. Some days I almost believe her.

Tyrone See you in class, Dais.

Mr Johnson Miss Davis!

Daisy Hate it when teachers calls me that.

Mr Johnson A word, if you please.

Daisy I have a choice?

Mr Johnson Do I have a choice, what?

Daisy Do I have a choice, sir?

Mr Johnson What are those?

Daisy My ears.

Mr Johnson On your ears.

Daisy He means my earrings.

Mr Johnson You know the rules.

Daisy They're a present.

Mr Johnson Well you can give them to me for safekeeping.

Daisy They're from my dad!

— He eyes her up and down.

Mr Johnson I see them again, I'm confiscating them, Daisy.

Daisy All right, don't get your knickers in a twist. Sorry, don't get your knickers in a twist, sir.
Wait till he turns the corner ... put them straight back on again.

— Riiiiiiiiing.

Miss Lyons Good work, Daisy.
Daisy This is origami. It's the ancient Japanese art of paper folding. We did it a couple of weeks ago and Miss Lyons says I'm really good so she lets me sit with the book and teach myself. I'm making a crane. That's a type of bird, not like a crane on a building site. And I'm making mine the most beautiful crane anyone ever saw. You got to be precise. Can't rush it. People ain't got the patience. But I do. You pull out this bit to get the beak. Turn over this and ——
Miss Lyons Looks like we are seeing Good Daisy today.
Daisy Can I take this with me when I go?
Miss Lyons Mind if I ask why?
Daisy I want to give it to someone.
Teresa Giving it to Morell and I know what for.
Daisy Shut up!

— Oooooooooh!

Miss Lyons You don't have to say who it is if you don't want.
Daisy But I do want. The words rise up, try to force their way out my gut, climbing up my throat into my mouth.
Miss Lyons Something you want to tell me, Daisy?
Daisy No, miss. Thanks, miss.

— Riiiiiiiinnng.

Tyrone Apparently, right, Natalie Baynes says Jerome Casey was outside Tomlinson's office.
Daisy Tyrone's always got the gossip.
Tyrone And he heard Tomlinson telling Miss Jennings that police are saying they need to send everyone home 'cause the buses aren't running and shops are closing and they're putting a curfew out 'cause there's gonna be trouble.

— What kind of trouble?

Daisy Do you mind? This is private.

— Sorry.

Daisy We're waiting for Mr Lennox. He's always late. Think he's got a
bit of a drink problem — then again, he does teach Geography, so ...
Tyrone Oh what?
Daisy Johnson.
Mr Johnson Mr Lennox has come down with a bug and had to go
home.
— Probably drunk.

Mr Johnson And that's a detention.
Daisy Everyone quiets down.
Mr Johnson I'll be taking his class instead.
Tyrone Sir, it true school's cancelled for the afternoon? 'Cause of the
shooting. Police think there might be trouble.
Mr Johnson If school is cancelled, Tyrone, we'll be sure to let you
know.

— Daisy kisses her teeth.

Mr Johnson Mr Lennox has been kind enough to leave this lesson plan
which I would like one of you to read out for me ...
Daisy Everyone looks round. Couple of the keen kids have their hands
up. Then I remember. My earrings! Turn, try and cover my ears ——
Mr Johnson I thought we'd spoken about those earrings, Miss Davis.
Daisy But sir, they're my ——
Mr Johnson No buts or there'll be another detention.
Daisy Sniggers while I hand them over, Teresa's loving it. Some dumb
worksheet about Brownian motion, pictures of atoms packed together,
bumping and bouncing off one another cause they ain't got enough
space, generating heat or some nonsense. Least that's what I should
be looking at. Instead I'm folding. Short little tail. Smooth along the
crease. Clean lines, don't want no wrinkles. Run my finger down the
spine, for a moment, I swear I feel it wriggle, like it's puffing itself up,
getting ready to take flight. But it ain't. Paper don't come to life. No
such thing as magic. This is all we got.

— Tyrone. Tyrone.

Tyrone What?

— Ping Ping Ping.

Daisy Messages left right and centre, kids arranging hook ups, orchestrating madness, all sorts.

— It true what I heard?

Tyrone You'll get us in trouble.

— Is school gonna be cancelled?
Tyrone That's what Natalie said.

— Natalie don't know nothing.

Mr Johnson What's going on?
Daisy Oh man.
Mr Johnson Daisy, phone.
Daisy Wasn't even me, it was them lot leaning over.
Mr Johnson Come on, phone.
Tyrone It's true, Sir, she was making a crane.
Mr Johnson Making a what?
Daisy Nice one, Tyrone.
Tyrone A crane, sir, she's really talented.
Teresa You fancy her or what?
Tyrone Shut up, man.
Mr Johnson Show me what you were making.
Daisy Sir, I'll put it away, I promise.
Mr Johnson Show me or it's detention.
    Very nice. You can have it back at the end of the week.
Daisy The week!
Mr Johnson First the earrings, then this, you know how the merit system works.
Daisy Can't wait till the end of the week, that's a whole ... week away.
Mr Johnson Give me one good reason why not?
Daisy Mind your own business.
Mr Johnson What did you say?
Daisy I said mind your own business, sir.
Mr Johnson Give it here.
Daisy No.
Mr Johnson Give it here.
Daisy No.
Mr Johnson I said give it.
Daisy And I said no! This is my paper crane, this is my bird, I made it and besides, it ain't for me, and you can't just go round taking things don't belong to you. That's the rules.

Mr Johnson I'll be phoning your mother.
Daisy See if I care.
Tyrone Daisy.
Daisy Just when the tension can't get no bigger, just when I think I can't take no more, just when I think I'm finally gonna break, say "Screw you Mr Johnson, screw you and your dumb haircut and your dumb rules and your dumb school —— "
Mr Tomlinson Attention! Attention!
— Tomlinson's voice from the tannoy.

Mr Tomlinson Due to recent incidents and following advice from the police it has been decided that a curfew will be in place in the borough this evening. As a consequence, lessons for the rest of the day are suspended ——
Daisy Desks slam, books in bags, and we don't hear no more cause we are gone.
Mr Johnson Don't think this gets you off the hook! I'm phoning your mother, Daisy. I'll speak to your mother about this. Come back! Come back!
Daisy Shout all you like. I got a delivery to make.

SCENE 4

— **Scene Four.**
— **In which Daisy and Tyrone evade ... the Inspector**

Inspector Oyster cards and tickets! Oyster cards and tickets!
Daisy Curfew starts in a few hours so the streets are a-hustle with the bustle of the people making their way home. Argos. Cash Converter. Superdrug.
Inspector Oyster cards and tickets.

The Inspector continues to inspect

Daisy All this traffic, so slow, this heat, bus smells like the armpit of some mangy dog or Johnson's coffee breath when he leans over the desk.
Johnson Let me check your work.
Daisy Everyone look so miserable, what's your problem? We alive, ain't we?
Tyrone Why we going Catford for?
Daisy Always questions.

Tyrone I known Daisy time. Always sat next to each other, even in little school. 'Member this one time, I called round Daisy's, she was upstairs getting changed so I sat talking to her mum in the kitchen and she said:

Bev Promise me you'll look after her, Tyrone. See too much of myself in her. You promise me you'll do that?

Tyrone Yes, I said. Yes, Mrs Davis.

Bev Call me Bev.

Tyrone That's what she said. Call me Bev. She's nice, Daisy's mum. Me? I want to be an architect. Build houses people can afford 'cause where me and Daisy live (*he kisses his teeth*). Tesco trolleys, rubbish, discarded nappies, burnt out cars. People don't respect their environment 'cause they don't respect themselves, that's what my dad says, "Why should anyone else believe in you if you don't believe in yourself?"

— Beep.

Daisy BBM from Morell.

Tyrone I don't like him.

Daisy You don't know him.

Tyrone And you do?

Daisy Just think sometimes people ain't what they seem.

Tyrone She turns away, stares out the window at the dust and heat.

Inspector Oyster cards and tickets. Oyster cards and tickets. Oyster cards and tickets.

Daisy Oh man.

Tyrone What?

Daisy I ain't got no Oyster card.

Tyrone Why not?

Daisy I don't like the idea of all these people tracking me. Why should the Mayor know who I am, that's creepy, T?

Tyrone How you even get on without a pass?

Daisy Slipped by when that old lady was burrowing about in her bag.

Inspector (*to Tyrone*) Oyster card. Thank you. Madam?

Daisy Left it at home.

Tyrone People are looking.

Daisy Why you persecuting me, why you giving me this hassle?

Inspector I'm not persecuting you, I just want to see your Oyster card.

Daisy I'm on special business.

Inspector And what sort of business would that be?

Daisy If you must know, I'm a young person's ticket inspector inspector.

Tyrone Oh my days.

Inspector A what?
Daisy The Mayor himself has appointed me personally to inspect the
 people who are looking at our tickets. And could I just say, Inspector,
 you're doing a marvellous job, keep up the good work.
Inspector All right, Chief Inspector, I get the idea. Now off the bus and
 we'll leave it at that.
Daisy Well that's convenient 'cause this is my stop now anyway.

SCENE 5

— **Scene Five.**
— **Roy's gaff.**

— Who's Roy?
— Watch the play, man, you'll find out.
— Sorry.
— So dumb, and stop playing with your phone, we're more than half
 way, all right?

Tyrone How much steps, man? Daisy, how many steps?
Daisy No one asked you to be here.
Tyrone How much longer though?
Daisy I told you, seventh floor.
Tyrone How many is that to go?
Daisy You can count, can't you?
Tyrone Finally. What number?
Daisy Seventy-five. Blue door.
Tyrone Seventy-five ... Blue door.
Daisy I hear someone in the flat. Music. A song I don't know. Tyrone,
 make yourself useful, knock on that door.
Tyrone You knock.
Daisy You're right there.
Tyrone You're closer.
Daisy Only 'cause you just took a step back.
Tyrone I never.
Daisy I saw you.
Tyrone That is rubbish, I —

— KNOCK KNOCK KNOCK KNOCK KNOCK.

Tyrone All right, no answer, can we go?
Jacqui Hello.

Daisy She's pretty. Only a few years older than me. Nineteen. Twenty.
I'm looking for Roy.

Tyrone Who's Roy? I think but don't say.

Daisy Kisses her teeth. Chews her gum. Thinks I'm one of Roy's girls.

Jacqui Ain't no Roy here.

Daisy He been here though.

Jacqui How you know?

Daisy I can read him on your face. Only people look that vexed is
vexed because of Roy. That man has an unrivalled capacity for vexing
people. When Roy is in the vicinity, vexation abounds.

Tyrone Come on, Daisy, maybe we should ——

Jacqui Bit young, ain't yer? Even for Roy.

Daisy Bite my tongue. Ain't got to justify nothing.
You Jacqui?
She don't like that. No one likes being named. Now it's my turn to be
surprised.

Jacqui You must be Daisy.

Daisy How you know that?

Jacqui He talks about you.

Daisy Roy?

Jacqui Who else?

Daisy So you seen him?

Jacqui Not for time.

Daisy A little boy, pretty face, maybe four, clings to her leg, little brown
eyes staring up.
Hello, I say, trying to give him a look that says, "Don't be afraid. I
won't do you no harm, I'm not like the others."

Jacqui Go back, Shaun. Play with your farm.

Daisy He looks me in the eye, trying to figure me out like I'm a puzzle,
like he seen something in me he recognizes, then darts back inside,
that little dopey off balance run that kids got.
Is he —— ?

Jacqui No. He's not Roy's. This your boyfriend?

Daisy No.

Jacqui What's he doing here?

Tyrone Daisy's my friend.

Jacqui I see. Well take it from me, Daisy. Friends are hard to come by.
You should stick with this one.

Daisy (*to Tyrone*) Stop smiling, you idiot. (*To Jacqui*) Where can I find
him?

Jacqui Try The Hawk.

Tyrone The Hawk?

Jacqui It's up next to Jackson's, by the green opposite Mecca Bingo.

Daisy I know where it is.
Jacqui Well you shouldn't. How old are you?
Daisy Old enough.
Jacqui Yeah, that's the problem. These days everyone's old enough.
  He's normally in there. If not, they'll know where to find him.
Daisy The old madness rises up, my mouth runs dry, I'm angry, so
  angry. I don't know why 'cause she's being nice to me.
Tyrone Come on, Dais, let's go.
Daisy As I leave she says:
Jacqui You take care, you hear me?
Daisy Who she think she is, telling me to take care?
Jacqui And if you see Roy, tell him he owes me rent.

SCENE 6

— **Scene Six.**
— **The Hawk.**

— Shunk. Shunk. Shunk.

Daisy Afternoon heat gives way to something different, air's getting
  heavy, people scuttling like rats round an old house, trying to get back
  in their holes before whatever is going to start starts. Cheap electronics
  stores, grocery stores push their shutters down. I got the march on.
Tyrone Daisy.
Daisy Snatches of gossip cut through the air like knives.

— Gonna be trouble.
— Police are out.
— Something's brewing.

Daisy And they're right.

— Camden.
— Acton.
— Croydon.
— Woolwich.
— London Fields.

Daisy The clans are gathering, but ain't no tribes tonight.
Tyrone Daisy.

Daisy If BBM was mad before, now it's going berserk, messages bouncing back and forth, filling the air like them molecules in science. Police trying to make sense of it but there's too much transmissions, always two steps behind.

Tyrone Daisy.

Daisy More shops shutting, key cutters, dry cleaners, charity shops full of old dresses and dead men's jackets. And then —

— The Hawk.

Daisy With its frosted glass and men outside with stares and tattoos and a little kid playing with a pink shoe.

— Hawk don't stop for nothing.

Tyrone Daisy!

Daisy Missed calls from my mum, texts piling up, RU OK? Everything all right? Please call me.

— Landlord's name above the door.

— Licences, weights, measures.

Tyrone Daisy!

Daisy What?

Tyrone Who's Roy?

Daisy Who is Roy? I guess you know by now.

Tyrone Daisy, wait.

Daisy Sort of half expected everyone would look up, but no. Guys slumped in chairs, staring up at Sky News. Most of them look dead. Maybe they are. Lady on TV in a red blouse and a concerned face, LONDON ON ALERT, the word EXPERT flashes up, someone else I never heard of.

Tyrone What we even doing here?

Daisy I'm clutching the paper crane by its wing. Wish Miss was here with me now.

Yvonne You all right, darling?

Daisy Says the lady behind the bar. Got one of them faces looks prettier without make up. Warm voice, strong arms, Celtic band across the top.

Yvonne Looking for someone?

Daisy Says it like she ain't even fazed, like this is normal, like it's an everyday thing some fourteen — sorry, fifteen — year-old kids wandering in. Maybe it is. Tyrone is phasing out, eyes glazing, he ain't got the hardness, not everyone does. Teachers talk about my estate like we all the same — they don't live here. Tough people, nice people, soft people, good people, bad people, hard-working people. But no one ever notices us until they get scared so that's all they see — their own fear magnified back. I'm looking for Roy.

Yvonne Roy?

Tyrone Who's Roy?

Daisy She looks sad.

Yvonne You must be Daisy.

Daisy How come everyone know my name?

Yvonne Heard a lot about you.

Daisy Oh yeah.

Yvonne You're even prettier than Roy says.

Tyrone Roy who?

Daisy For someone who gets good marks at school, Tyrone sure can act dumb.

Yvonne Jackson's, next door. He'll be back in a minute.

Tyrone What's Jackson's, that a newsagent?

Daisy I can guess.

Yvonne It's a betting shop, love. Gone to place a bet. You want to wait? I get you a Coke? Or a sandwich?

Daisy Nah, it's all right.

Yvonne It's on the house.

Landlord Mick That's coming out your wages.

Yvonne Shut up, Mick. You want something to eat?

Tyrone I'll have one.

Daisy Shut up, Tyrone. She's nice. You forget that sometimes. That most people, however tough they come, underneath is just nice.

Tyrone Door swings open, light spills in, kind of light you get when the sun hits the top of buildings and just spreads, an orange glow, like the city's on fire.

Daisy And just like that he's there.

Tyrone Silhouetted against the doorway.

Daisy Holding on to the door frame like that kid clinging on to his mum's leg. Then it comes. Big man swagger. Chest puffed out, belly, bandy-legged strides, brushes his nose with his hand, sniffs like men do when they scared. Paper under his arm, see the biro where he's marked the dogs from here.

— Roy.

Roy So what you doing here?

Daisy He says, trying to sound all casual.

Roy Yvonne, you met my little girl, Daisy? Met my little girl?

Daisy My little girl. I could take issue with every one of them three
words. My. Little. Girl.

Tyrone Yvonne nods.

Yvonne She's beautiful, Roy.

Roy Hey everyone, this my girl Daisy — this my girl!

Daisy A few heads look up and nod and grunt then go back to their
drinks.

Roy Who's this then, your boyfriend?

Daisy This my friend, Tyrone.

Roy Pleased to make your acquaintance, Tyrone.

Daisy It's how he talks, I swear.

Roy Yvonne, let's have a drink, usual and two cokes for my little girl
and my man Tyrone here.

Daisy Yvonne looks at Roy then at me. He ain't got no money. She
sighs, gets us drinks, landlord looks up from his paper — this is
coming out her wages.

Roy What you doing here Daisy? How come you not in school?

Daisy Let us out early. 'Cause of the curfew.

Roy Like people gonna listen to that.

Daisy I say nothing.

Roy How you find me?

Daisy The woman.

Roy What woman?

Daisy There more than one?

Roy Oh, I see, you been to the flat. Jac told you all about me, did she,
told you what a bad man I am, poisoned your mind against me, just
like your mum did? That it, telling you lies, telling you stories?

Daisy Said you owed her money.

Roy She's always going on about money, thinks I owe her, ain't right
in the head.

Daisy Seemed all right to me.

Roy I miss you, Dais, miss seeing you. You miss me?

Daisy Hold open my hand.

Roy What is it? That for me?

Tyrone The paper crane.

Daisy I ain't gonna cry. Ain't gonna let that happen.

Roy Where you get this?

Daisy Told you, I made it.

Roy What you go and do that for?

Daisy Yvonne puts the drinks down, smiles a half smile, don't want her
pity, don't want no one's pity.

Roy Why you come here, see me like this?

Daisy You're my dad.

Roy But why today?

Tyrone He knows, right? He must know?

Daisy He don't. He really don't.

Tyrone It's her birthday. Today is her birthday.

Roy Course it is, course it —— been so busy, I got stuff going on right now, stuff I got to deal with.

Daisy I see that.

Roy Was going to get you something. I'll take you out, we'll, we'll do something.

Daisy Now?

Roy I can't now.

Daisy When?

Roy Soon.

Daisy How soon?

Roy There's a, there's a curfew, darling, nothing's open.

Daisy Could go to your flat, watch a DVD.

Roy I'm not staying at mine at the moment.

Yvonne Figures.

Roy Haven't you got some glasses to collect?

Daisy What you got that's so important? Who you got to meet?

Roy Don't be like that, Dais, it was great to see you.

Daisy You're going.

Roy I got to.

Daisy Why?

Roy Not in here, babe.

Daisy Why?

Roy I'm sorry.

Daisy And he leaves, like he always does, like he always did.
Wait.
He stops. You won't believe what happens next, he stops at the door and in front of everyone he says to me.

Roy Know what, Dais? I'll cancel the other thing. Let's go to the pictures, get out this heat? We'll get some popcorn and all the Coca Cola you want. I'll pay two quid extra so's we get the comfy seats, let's live it up. Only live once, right? And after we'll go Nando's you can have all the Peri Peri in the world and ice-cream and. ..

Daisy Go on. Why you stopped? Why you stopped?

— It's not what he did, Daisy.

Daisy Yeah it is.

— It ain't.

Daisy Tyrone, tell them. Tell them that's what happened. Tell them that's what he did.
Tyrone I can't.
Daisy Tell them.

— What does he say?

Tyrone He says:
Roy You couldn't lend us a couple of quid could you, Dais? Just to tide us over. Just need a couple of quid for something.
Daisy It's my birthday.
Roy Maybe your mum gave you some money or ——
Yvonne Roy.
Roy I'll call round later, I promise.
Daisy The door swings. This time he really is gone. Glance down at the counter. The paper crane. Didn't even take it.
Yvonne He does love you, darling.
Daisy Don't talk to me. Don't no one ever talk to me.
Tyrone You all right, Dais?

— Vvvvb. Vvvvb.

Daisy Another text from Mum. This one ends with a worried face. Course I'm all right. Why wouldn't I be all right?
Tyrone Let's go home.
Daisy Don't want to never go home.
Tyrone Feel the weight in the air, gonna be crazy tonight, Dais.
Daisy Streets quieter now. Few drinkers. Turkish guys who own the kebab shops, coffee shops, barber shops. They ain't scared of no one, the Turks. Couple of students come out a newsagent with pizza and beer, laughing and joking how it's all gonna kick off.

— Vvvvb. Vvvvb.

Daisy "Daisy Duke. Coming out to play?"
Tyrone Come on, Dais, let's go home. Watch this on the news.
Daisy I ain't watching nothing on the news. Wanna be part of it, need to do something, be someone.
Tyrone I don't know, it could get rough.

— Vrooooom!

Morell Daisy! Daisy Duke! Been looking all over!

Tyrone Morell pulls up, working the revs, like he's some kind of gangster in his uncle's borrowed car.

Morell You get my SMS?

Daisy Maybe.

Morell Ignoring me, that's cold.

Daisy Biding my time.

Tyrone Daisy.

Daisy Go home, Tyrone, this ain't for you.

Morell You getting in or what?

Daisy I look at the car. At Morell's gap-toothed grin. Then at T with his eyes saying / "No, Daisy. Please, Daisy. Don't, Daisy."

Tyrone (*mouthing the words, simultaneous with Daisy*) No, Daisy. Please, Daisy. Don't, Daisy.

Daisy Nothing else going on.

Morell Hop in.

Tyrone Can't leave her like this. Said I'd take care of her. I promised.

Morell Hey, who said you could get in my car?

Tyrone You want me to go, you gonna have to drag me out.

Daisy Morell's older and bigger, he could dash Tyrone if he wanted and Tyrone knows it. But Morell ain't the type to get his hands dirty.

Morell Don't get nothing on my back seat, you get me?

Tyrone Why, would your uncle not be pleased?

Morell I'm this close ...

Daisy Morell flexes his engine, looks over to check I'm impressed, and you know what, I am. Blood in my veins, finally I'm alive, we could do anything, I think, I say it out loud, I shout it. We could do anything!

Morell Yeah baby.

Tyrone As we speed off in Morell's big red car that ain't as good as he thinks he is, I glance out the window as we pass The Hawk. And through the glass of the betting shop next door — Jackson's — I see Daisy's dad, staring at the screens. He glances this way. Tries to make like he ain't seen us, but he has. Daisy acts like she don't know he's looking but she knows. She always knows.

SCENE 7

— Scene Seven.
— In which Daisy and Morell mash up JD sports and emerge with some quality items.

Daisy Morell's nodding his head like he got some fat stereo but the bass ain't nothing, got a tinny sound like a phone in a biscuit tin.

Morell Look.

Daisy Primark, KFC, JD Sports. We're in the retail park, where we go of a Saturday. Shoppers piling out, black, white, brown, all kinds of people, men, women, young, old.

Tyrone Shops ain't shut after all.

— Morell holds out a finger.

Morell Nah, man, windows all broke.

Daisy First I don't get what Morell means. People in cars driving past so calm. Then I see. Shutters forced up, glass on the ground. They busted these shops open, people are helping themselves.

Tyrone Some granny holds aloft a pair of Nikes —

Daisy And no one doing a thing about it.

Tyrone She's putting them on, someone's granny putting on some Nikes!

Daisy On the pavement, two girls compare trackie bottoms they just bought, pulling them out of JD Sports bags, can't be more than nine. They got bags. Bags!

Daisy Where you get them bags from?

Girl Uh. JD Sports.

Daisy One of them says, pointing at the label like we dumb. It's so calm, it's so normal. Just like Sunday shopping, people chatting.

Tyrone How come Feds aren't around?

Girl 2 Down the town centre, protecting the proper shops.

Daisy Proper shops. 'Cause JD Sports don't count. KFC don't count. All Feds care about is where the real people go, not this discount retail nonsense. As Morell parks up, someone shoves a microphone in the face of the two girls.

Writer Could you tell me what this means to you?

Girl Who are you?

Girl 2 Where you from?

Writer I'm from a theatre company, we're responding to events.

Girl What you making, a play?

Girl 2 You write for TV?

Writer We're trying to find out what you really think?

Girl Done anything I've heard of?

Writer I know some people who write for *Skins*.

Girl 2 Do you know anyone famous?

Girl You got their phone number?

Girls (*together*) Can we be in your play?

Daisy On the shop floor, people help each other pick clothes. It's all so civilized.

— After you.
— No, after you, Claude.
— No, after you.

Daisy In the store room some lady tries to reach the kids' shoes, a guy in a hoodie steps up and says—

— Can I help you?

Tyrone Like he's a shop assistant or something. Maybe he is, maybe this what he does on his day off, help out at events of civil unrest, make sure events proceed in an orderly fashion.

— Thank you.
— You're welcome.

Daisy Think I'd look good in this?
Morell Yeah, Daisy Duke, try it on.
Daisy What, here?
Morell Changing rooms. I'll stand watch.
Daisy Step inside the last free cubicle, hear two girls laughing in the next one along, pull the tracksuit on under my skirt then take the skirt off. Put the top over my school shirt, pull my hair back, look at the girl in the mirror. She looks like me. But nicer. This what it's like to be rich, to be one of them girls at school who gets a lift in a nice car and who goes home to a nice house? It's a nice feeling, feeling special. No, not special. Normal. Just normal. Like I belong. How I look?
Tyrone You look good.

— He says, mouth open.
— And she says:

Daisy Where's Morell?
Morell What a buzz, man, what a buzz! We taken JD Sports man! We own this place!
Daisy He's got a wild look in his eyes, Morell, like something got him, something dangerous, something he just can't keep to himself.
Morell We can do what we want! We can do anything we want! And no one gets to tell us what to do, ever again!
Tyrone Morell kicks a couple of shop dummies hard, sending them toppling.
Guy Hey, watch what you're doing, bruv.
Morell Some guy step to me. Does he not know who he's dealing with? I hear my uncle's voice in my ear. What you gonna do about it, André?

You gonna be a man? he says. Or you gonna be some pussy boy like
you always was? Man's taking you for a mug. You gonna allow that?
Who's he think he is? You some kind of fool?

— Morell takes a step.

Guy We got a problem?

— The other guy takes a step.

Morell Yeah, I got a problem, man, my problem is you, little bitch.

— Everyone take a breath.

Tyrone And now we do have a problem, 'cause this other guy, he ain't
backing down and you can tell he ain't messing 'cause while Morell's
all shouting and raving and waving, this guy is calm. Like he does this
all the time. Like he knows how the story ends.
Guy You need to settle down. Don't front up to people when you don't
know who it is you're talking to, you get me?

— And just like that, Morell looks like a little boy, 'cause this guy's
bigger and older and uglier and he ain't going nowhere. Morell looks
small, like he's shrinking.

Morell It was an accident. No big deal, yeah, we're all cool.
Guy One of these days your friend gonna get you in trouble.
Morell Come on.

— Says Morell.

Morell This place is full of nobodies.

Scene 8

— **Scene Eight.**
— **In which Morell won't take no for an answer.**

Daisy Roll down the street in Morell's uncle's car, people pushing
shopping trollies carrying clothes, TVs, radios, overhead helicopter
blades mow the air like summer grass. There's an energy.

Tyrone Up in the windows, curtains twitching, all the real people having a good sniff, some of them got their phones out, filming us.

Daisy Hello!

Tyrone Hello!

Morell We can see you!

Daisy Curtains snap shut. Makes me laugh. Today we're the real people and you're the ones hiding away. How'd you like that? See Teresa, the one who hates me. As we pass I scream, I'm alive, I'm alive, I'm alive. Gives me the finger but I don't see her in no fancy car.

Morell You know, I was this close to dropping that fool.

Daisy Almost forgotten about Morell he'd been quiet so long.

Morell He was lucky I was having a nice day, else I'd have messed him up.

Tyrone Mess him up? I saw the look on your face, only thing you was going to mess up was your trousers.

— BANG.

Daisy Morell slams the dashboard hard.

— Eeeeeeerrrrrrrrr.

Daisy Car screeches to a halt outside a shop.

Everyone except Morell and Tyrone takes a breath

Morell One more word. Just one. You get me?

Daisy Hadn't noticed where we were. Shutters are up. It's open.

Morell I'm thirsty.

Daisy Push past the sign saying "One child at a time" and —

Akhtar Should be closed. There's problems at the retail place but that's streets away, anyway, visiting hours at the hospital don't start for another hour, besides, why shouldn't I be open? This is my home.

— Ting ting.

Akhtar It's that girl from earlier, Daisy, with two other boys. The younger one I know. The older one used to come in here with his uncle, dragging him by the arm, calling him all sorts of names.
Only one at a time. You can see the sign, can't you? Only one at a time.

Morell We'll be out your way soon enough old man.

Akhtar We're closed.

Morell Don't look closed to me. Look closed to you?

Daisy No. It don't.

Akhtar Please, only one at a time.

Morell Says one child at a time. Calling me a child?

Daisy Ain't so brave now, Mr Akhtar.

Tyrone Morell walks along the aisle, flicks off a couple of magazines with his hand.

Daisy Treat me like a second class citizen. How you feel about your two pence now? How you feel about that?

Akhtar Pick those up.

Morell Bottle of rum. I said I want a bottle of rum.

Akhtar You can't have it.

— Slam.

Daisy Morell shoves a ten pound note down on the counter.

Morell Come on, man, half of rum, don't mess me around.

Akhtar I need to see some ID.

Morell ID? ID? You see that BM parked outside? That's my ID right there.

Akhtar I need to see some ID. I cannot serve you without ID.

Morell Don't be a fool, man, I got money.

Akhtar Please, I just need some identification. A passport or —

Morell Passport! I ain't got no passport!

Akhtar Or ID card.

Morell Just gimme the rum and I'll be out your face.

Akhtar I cannot serve you, it's the law.

Tyrone Just serve him, man!

Morell What's this fool doing? Can't he see no one wants this. But when someone fronts you down — what do they expect?

Akhtar People can't just come in here and tell me what to do.

Daisy Heart's beating so fast.

Morell All I hear is my uncle in my head telling me never to back down, never to be a pussy.

Akhtar I would like you to leave.

Morell Just give me the rum.

Akhtar You shouldn't be drinking.

— BANG.

Daisy Slams his hand down on the counter a second time.

Morell Did I ask for your opinion? You don't want people to buy it, don't sell it. Look at you, selling dirty magazines, who are you to get all high and mighty?

Akhtar I'm just trying to make a living.

Morell All I want is the rum. Do you understand me?

Akhtar Please leave my shop.

Morell I ain't leaving till I get my rum.

Akhtar My wife is sick. I need to go so I can visit her, will you please leave?

Morell Tyrone, watch the door.

Tyrone Why, what you gonna do?

Morell Watch the door!

Tyrone What you gonna ——

Daisy My stomach's doing butterflies.

Morell I ain't leaving without my rum.

Tyrone Daisy, let's go, this ain't worth it.

Daisy And I don't know why but for whatever reason I hear myself say — I'm staying.

Tyrone I made a promise. I made a promise I would look after her. I'm sorry.

— Ting ting.

Morell I'm gonna ask once more. I got money. Give me that rum.

Daisy Just me and Morell now.

Akhtar No.

Morell Gonna leave the money here, yeah, I ain't no thief. I'm just gonna take the rum.

Daisy Can't he see he just don't want to lose face! Let him have it! I say.

Akhtar Get out! Get out of my shop! Get out of my shop!

Daisy And then it happens, so fast I can barely compute. Morell reaches round the counter to grab the rum, Mr Akhtar slaps his arm away —

— Bang.

Daisy Not even a punch, a slap, a slap to the head and Mr Akhtar's head hits the shelves behind him. Bottles fall from the shelves, smashing round his feet. He tries to hit back but this just makes Morell more vex and he hits Mr Akhtar, properly this time and —

— Bang.

Daisy He's down. He kicks him. Again. And again. And again. He's crying, Mr Akhtar, he's crying, Morell's shouting his head off.

Morell Shouldn't have done that. All I wanted was the rum. What was I supposed to do? It's your fault. It's your fault.

Daisy I don't know if he's talking to Akhtar or me. Thought it would be a buzz, thought it would be fun. We grab the rum and we run straight out the door and we get in the car and we ——

— That ain't what happened

Daisy And we get in the car and we ——

— That ain't what happened.

Daisy And we drive like we ——

— That ain't how it went.

Daisy We get in the car and we drive like we ——
We get in the car and we ——
We get in the car and we ——
You don't know what it's like.

— What happened, Daisy?

Daisy They closed the youth centre.

— What happened?

Daisy We ain't got no EMA. Got nowhere to go, every day, no jobs no nothing.

— That's just excuses.

Daisy You don't live here.

— I tried to run.
— I wanted to leave, but Morell shouted.

Morell No one leaves till I say.

— Why d'you listen to him?

Daisy I was scared.
Morell Look at this fool, look at him. Think he's bad this old man, think he's bad.
Daisy And he spat on him.

— Like that.
— Spat on him.
— Mr Akhtar, crying like a baby.

Morell Now you.
Daisy Now me what?
Morell Spit on him.
Daisy I don't want to.
Morell Go on, spit.
Daisy Wanted me to share the blame so it ain't just on him.
Morell Spit!
Daisy You're hurting me!
  He grabbed my arm, felt the skin bruise.
Morell Spit. Spit!
Daisy With his eyes, Mr Akhtar's saying / please.
Akhtar Please. / Please.
Daisy Please.

— And did you?

Daisy No. No.
  No.
  No.
  Yes.

— Ting ting.

Morell What a buzz, man, what a buzz, you see the look on his face?
  You feel that? You see how scared he is? I shoulda filmed it, shoulda
  got it on my phone.
Daisy He was crying.
Morell He attacked me. You saw, right, he made the first move.
Daisy Morell up loud on Morell's biscuit tin radio. We pass people carrying
  more things they ain't paid for. What's this got to do with a man got shot
  other side of town, what's this got to do with me? Four more missed calls.
  All mum. I think of tea and toast. Sunpat spread thick and butter.
Morell Thought we could go back to mine?
Daisy What?
  We're at the lights. Engine's humming. Whole town gone crazy but
  Morell's still observing the Highway Code.
Morell Thought we could go back to mine? Drink some rum, see what
  happens?
Daisy He looks at me. I mean *looks* at me, the way boys do when they
  stop being boys and turn into something else.

Morell Get some privacy. Know what I'm saying?
Daisy My mum always said a bad man is just a man who done wrong
so many times he forget there ever was a choice.
I see the lights going the other direction start to turn and realize this
is it. Our light is about to change. Go left? Or go right? Before I even
realize what I'm doing, fling wide the door and running down the road
away from Morell and this time I really do run. I run until my lungs
burst. Then I run some more.

SCENE 9

— **The second to last scene.**
— **Where Tyrone gives Daisy her birthday present.**

Tyrone Where you been?
Daisy It's getting late. My legs are tired, must have been walking for
hours. Tyrone sat on a wall near my house.
Tyrone What happened? Daisy, what happened?
Daisy Don't want to talk about it.
Tyrone Are you all right? Is Mr Akhtar all right? Is he ——
Daisy He's fine,
I say. Don't even know if I'm lying or not.
Tyrone Where's Morell?
Daisy I left him.
Tyrone Did he do something to you? Did he do something?
Daisy Such a good friend, Tyrone. My only friend.
Think I might have done something stupid.
Tyrone You have sex with him?
Daisy No.
Tyrone You all right?
Daisy Stop saying that!
Tyrone But are you?
Daisy He says, voice soft.
Tyrone Your mum's worried.
Daisy You talk to her?
Tyrone Yeah.
Daisy What you say?
Tyrone Nothing. I was worried, that's all. She been calling you. I been
calling you.
Daisy I look at my phone. Battery's gone. Nothing left to give.
Tyrone It's all over the news.
Daisy What is?

Tyrone There's people analyzing it like it's a game of football.
Daisy Where you get them sweatbands from?
Tyrone They look all right on me.
Daisy You thief them?
Tyrone Everyone was doing it.
Daisy Can't help smiling. Always makes me smile, Tyrone. He's handsome, I never noticed. Never noticed lots of things.
Tyrone You left this in the pub. Well, your dad left it but — I thought you might want it.

— He hands Daisy the paper crane.

Tyrone Happy birthday, Daisy.
Daisy Will you come by later?
Tyrone I don't know. Think I might be in trouble with my dad. I'll see.
Daisy Stands there looking at me, Tyrone. Before I start to cry, I go.

SCENE 10

— The final scene. Daisy comes home for her tea.

Daisy Says nothing when I come in, Mum. Just comes over, kisses my head, sits me down. While the kettle boils she stares at me, her eyes so bright. She spoons in the sugar, adds the milk. Sets it down, so careful. So precise. No one makes tea like Mum. Streetlamp haze burns gently through the window.
Bev Where you get them clothes?
Daisy Smells of smoke in here. The ashtray's full.
Bev Oh Daisy. We are gonna have to talk, you know? Where you been? Who you been with? Where you get that?
Daisy I made it in class.
Bev You made it?
Daisy Yeah.
Bev I used to do this with you. We got a book out from the library once. Origami. When you was little. Used to love doing that. Probably don't remember. I got you a present. It's in the next room. Maybe when you finished your tea.
Daisy What have I done? What have I done?

— Bang bang bang.

Daisy A heavy knock at the front door.

Bev You expecting anyone?

Daisy No. Not really.

She smiles, trying to look calm, but she's turning her lighter over in her hand over and over. It's catching, fear.

Bev I'll just see who it is.

Daisy She leaves her lighter on the table. I stare at it, and suddenly, with a mug of my mum's tea in my hand, I'm the loneliest person in the world. Maybe it's the police. Maybe it's Tyrone. Maybe it's Dad finally got his act together, I don't know. I don't know. I think of Tomlinson. And Miss Lyons. And my dad's girlfriend. The ticket inspector. JD Sports. Morell. And the lady in the bar with the kind eyes. And my paper crane. I pick up Mum's lighter. Flick the flame into life. And before I know it, the crane is burning, curling into ash, dissolving, dying. Things burning look so pretty, don't they?

Bev Daisy. Someone to see you.

Daisy I don't dare turn around. So I stand. Fists clenched. Eyes shut. Until a voice says —

— Daisy.

CURTAIN

Lightning Source UK Ltd.
Milton Keynes UK
UKHW022016170621
385696UK00006B/191